INTRODUCTION ...

- These student worksheets are intended to act alongside the corresponding revision guide to help reinforce your understanding and improve your confidence.

- Every worksheet is cross-referenced to
  'The Essentials of G.C.S.E Design and Technology: Graphic Products' edited by Debbie Eason

- The questions concentrate purely on the content you need to cover, and the limited space forces you to choose your answer carefully.

> These worksheets can be used ...
> ... as <u>classwork sheets</u> where pupils use their revision guide to provide the answers ...
> ... as <u>harder classwork sheets</u> where pupils study the topic first, then answer the questions without their guides ...
> ... as easy to mark <u>homework sheets</u> which test understanding and reinforce learning ...
> ... as the basis for <u>learning homeworks</u> which are then tested in subsequent lessons ...
> ... as <u>test material</u> for topics or entire modules ...
> ... as a <u>structured revision programme</u> prior to the exams.

- Remember to fill in your score at the bottom of each page in the small grey box ⬜ , and also to put your score in the 'marks' column on the contents page.

EDITED BY:	RUSSEL JONES

Principal examiner for Graphic Products at G.C.S.E.
Head of Design and Technology at Don Valley High School, Doncaster.

1. What are the common materials used to make Graphic Products?

(i) _____

(ii) _____

(iii) _____

2. Why are pictures and text used in Graphic Design?

Pictures: _____

Text: _____

3. (a) What is meant by 'typeface'?

_____

(b) List five different effects which can alter the look of text.

(i)   C _ _ _ T _ _ S

(ii) B _ _ _ _

(iii) R _ _ _ _ _ _ _ _   _ _ _

(iv) _ _ _ _ _ W

(v)   _ _ T _ _ _ _

4. Look carefully at any breakfast cereal packet eg. corn flakes, sketch it and explain how the images and typeface add to the product.

Sketch of cereal box

1. Complete the following sentences.

(i) A drawing board and T-square are used to draw _____ drawings.

(ii) Used with a T-square, _____ allow lines at specific angles (90°, 60°/30° and 45°) to be drawn.

(iii) Angles are measured with a _____ .

2. Rearrange the following graphite pencil grades in order of hardness. (One has been placed for you)

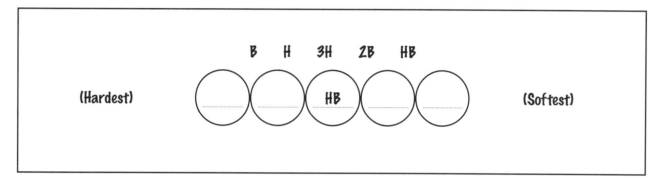

B   H   3H   2B   HB

(Hardest)   HB   (Softest)

3. Which grade(s) of graphite pencil is used for the following?

USE	GRADE	
Drawing construction lines		
Simple shading and toning		
Quick, freehand sketching		

4. (a) Fibre-tipped pens can leave a 'tide' mark on the paper. What is meant by the term 'tide' mark?

(b) Some spirit and water-based felt pens 'bleed' when used on some types of paper.
What is meant by the term 'bleed' in this sense?

5. Give an advantage of using a circle template.

6. Name a computer software drawing (CAD) program you have used.

1. Drawing paper sizes are classified as the 'A' series. The largest sheet in the 'A' series is A0.

> (i) What is the area of a sheet of A0 paper? ....
>
> (ii) What is the recommended size of paper
>   for a Graphic Products design folder? ....

2. A diagram of paper sizes is shown. A3 size is given.

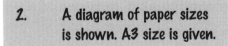

Write the appropriate 'A' series size in each space.

Paper size = ...

This is **A3 size**

3. An examination candidate, as part of a project, wants to make an A5 booklet from one sheet of A3 paper.

> How many separate A5 printed pages can be cut from one sheet of A3?
>
> ....

Paper size = ...

4. Paper and board are also graded by thickness or weight.

> (i) Name the unit used to measure thickness of board. ....
>
> (ii) Papers of different size can be compared by their 'grammage'. What units are used to express grammage?
>
> ....

1. Give typical weights for the following

(i) Drawing paper.
(ii) Modelling board.

(i)

(ii)

2. Complete the chart below for paper, card and board, showing their uses and properties.

TYPE OF PAPER OR BOARD	USES	PROPERTIES
Cartridge Paper	1. 2. 3.	1. 2.
	1. In preparation of final ideas	1. 2. 3.
	1. High quality presentations	1. 2.
Ink-jet card	1.	1.
Tracing Paper	1.	1. 2. 3.
	1.	1. Good strength for weight material
	1.	1. Pre-printed with lines at 30°/60° and 90°
	1. For working drawings	1.

3. (a) What is the disadvantage in using sugar paper for display work?

(b) Why is white board used to make book covers?

1. (a) What three things could you do to help the visual impact and continuity of your folder?

(i) _____ (ii) _____ (iii) _____

(b) What important information should there be on the cover of your folder?

(i) _____ (ii) _____ (iii) _____

(c) What important information should there be on every page of your folder?

(i) _____ (ii) _____ (iii) _____

(d) What is the advantage of having a 'simple' black border on your page?

_____

(e) It is recommended that the space from the paper's edge to the left border is wider than the others. Why?

_____

(f) A Contents Page is considered a good idea. Give two reasons why a contents page can help you towards a good grade.

(i) _____

(ii) _____

2. It is recommended that the folder should not be all ICT produced OR all hand drawn. Why is a mix of techniques considered the best?

_____

3. List FIVE appropriate ICT techniques and/or applications which could enhance a project.

(i) _____ (ii) _____ (iii) _____

(iv) _____ (v) _____

4. Why is it important that all your written communication is produced in a logical and well-organised manner?

_____

1. All graphic products are designed and made with a client in mind. Give two advantages of having a 'real' client.

(i) ....

(ii) ....

2. A Design Process in the form of a 'flow chart' should lead you through any project.

(i) Write one stage of the Design Process in each box (in any order)

(ii) From your list of stages above, arrange them in order for a successful project.

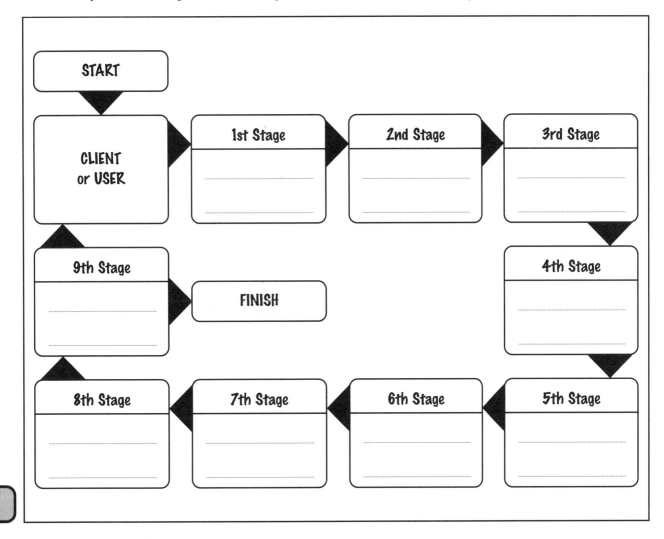

1. Brainstorming (an Ideas Web) is useful in deciding the type of problem you could investigate, and in exploring the possibilities of a particular project.

(a) Complete the brainstorming diagram (Ideas Web) for problem areas related to the promoting of a new 'sports, energy drink' (by adding ideas and links).

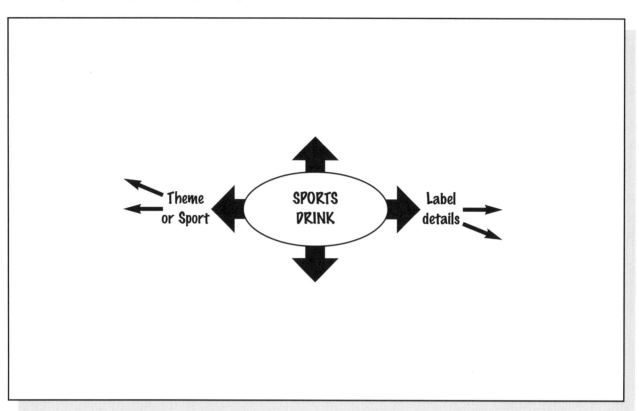

(b) Draw a brainstorming diagram (Ideas Web) for the design of a set of commemorative postage stamps.

1. A specification should reflect information found in which stage of the design process?

2. A good specification should be detailed enough to allow a 'third party' to start to plan and make the final project. What is meant by a 'third party'?

3. Good projects have a Design Specification and a Product Specification.

(i) What is a Design Specification?

(ii) What is a Product Specification?

4. Using either of the examples on the previous page write a **DESIGN SPECIFICATION** using 'bullet' points. (Write in the title of your chosen project)

My _____ will:

1. What is the difference between PRIMARY sources and SECONDARY sources?

2. Draw a brainstorming diagram (Ideas Web) which shows sources for researching into environmental issues.

3. Researching for a project can produce large amounts of material, brochures and data. Underline one of the following statements which would improve your grade.

(i) Include all information you have gathered.

(ii) Include all information you have gathered but highlight relevant details.

(iii) Include only relevant material.

(iv) Include only relevant material with notes and conclusions.

4. Questionnaires are a useful way to gather information or data, but need to be designed carefully. Fill in the gaps to complete the important features of a good questionnaire.

(i) Keep the questionnaire _____, about _____ good questions.

(ii) Questions should be _____ and not _____

(iii) Different _____ and _____ should not be offended.

(iv) Use _____ where possible and ask only _____ questions.

1. Why do designers analyse, test and evaluate existing products? Give two reasons.

(i) ....

(ii) ....

2. Study a small hand held electronic device. DO NOT TAKE IT APART. Sketch it and answer the following:

eg.

Sketch your device here

(i) What is the 'target group' of your chosen device?

....

(ii) What THREE features of your device appeal most to the target group?

● .... ● .... ● ....

(iii) Where would the device be sold?

....

(iv) Are the controls/displays well positioned?

....

(v) What materials is the device made from?

....

(vi) When new, how would it be packaged?

....

(vii) How does your device differ from a similar product?

....

1. Name FOUR different types of charts or graphs used to represent data.

(i) _____ (ii) _____

(iii) _____ (iv) _____

2. The table below states the distances that pupils have to travel to school.

DISTANCE	Up to 1 km	From 1 to 2 km	From 2 to 3 km	Over 3 km
NUMBER OF PUPILS	10	8	5	2

(a) What is the total number of pupils in the survey? _____

(b) Use the above data to complete the following charts. Name each type of chart.

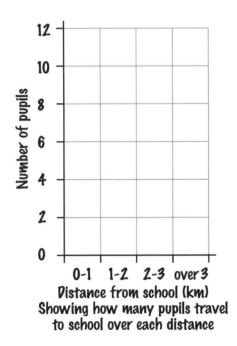

Number of pupils

0-1 1-2 2-3 over 3
Distance from school (km)
Showing how many pupils travel
to school over each distance

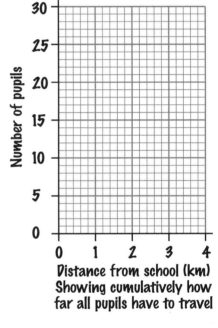

Number of pupils

0   1   2   3   4
Distance from school (km)
Showing cumulatively how
far all pupils have to travel

(i) This is a _____

(ii) This is a _____

3. Complete a pictogram using the data about the type of transport used by the pupils to get to school. Let one symbol be 20 pupils.

Nº of Pupils	Type of Transport
100	On Foot
50	Cycle
30	Car
20	Bus

Foot | Cycle | Car | Bus

1. Why should your ideas combine both sketches and brief notes?

2. A new vegetarian café called 'Roots' needs a new menu card design. In the space below sketch a range of first ideas for a menu card eg. outline, colour, style, shape etc.

'Initial' DESIGN IDEAS
for a menu card

ROOTS Veggie Cafe   Sheet 4   By J. Smith

3. Evaluation of ideas is important.

(i) Why refer your ideas to the 'Specification' ?

(ii) How can other people improve your initial ideas?

1. What is meant by the 'development' of a design?

2. Complete the ideas development sheet for a Vegetarian Burger box.
Consider materials, size, colour, position of any information, method of manufacture etc.

═══ DEVELOPMENT OF IDEAS ═══
Veggie Burger Box

ROOTS Veggie Cafe   Sheet 6   By J. Smith

1. Give THREE reasons why models are used.

(i) ....

(ii) ....

(iii) ....

2. Some computer programs can model 3-D products.
State an advantage and a disadvantage of computer generated models.

Advantage: ....

Disadvantage: ....

3. Which modelling materials are used for:

(i) an architectural model? ....

(ii) a coloured sign on a café frontage? ....

(iii) machining a model CD player? ....

(iv) hand shaping a camera? ....

(v) a quality box for a mobile phone? ....

(vi) covering a wire mesh frame? ....

4. Which modelling material can be 're-used'?

5. Give the correct names for the following modelling equipment.

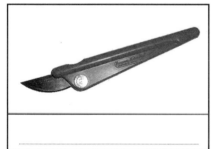

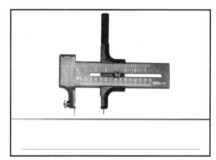

6. Give a safety rule which must be observed when

(i) cutting medium density fibreboard on a mechanical saw.

(ii) sawing acrylic.

1. Different adhesives, glues and cements are used for different materials and for different applications. Complete the following table.

Adhesive Type	Trade Name	Typical use in graphic products	Safety Considerations
Rubber-based Cement			
Glue Stick			Safe to use
		Gluing balsa wood models	
Hot Glue			
		Bonding card or wood	
		'Welding' Perspex	
			Fume extraction. Face mask.
Resin		Sticks most materials	

2. What do you understand by the term 'fixing' a drawing?

3. Briefly describe a method of 'masking' part of a drawing for airbrushing.

1. (a)(i) Draw and label a sketch of a photograph being encapsulated.

   (ii) Briefly describe how you would encapsulate a photograph.

   (i)

   (ii)

   (b) Name two Graphic products which would benefit from lamination/encapsulation.

   (i)   (ii)

2. A designer models a hand-held radio in modelling foam.
   Explain how a body filler can be used to improve its finish.

3. Name the two parts of an ink or paint.

   (i)   (ii)

4. List the four main groups of paints and inks.

   (i)   (ii)

   (iii)   (iv)

SKETCHING

1. In the space below sketch, freehand, the outline shape of an Easter Egg.

2. In the space below, complete the outline of a menu card holder by using the Thick/Thin line technique.

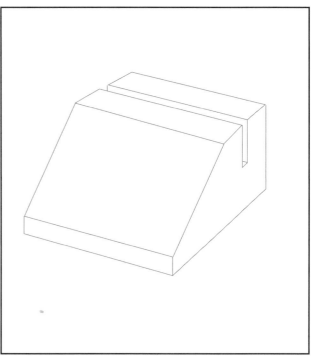

3. Use the Crating technique to draw a 3D sketch of this model car body ....

4. Why is it good examination technique to leave faint crating lines on your drawing?

1. What is rendering?

2. Using only one coloured pencil, shade the drawing below to make it look more 3D.

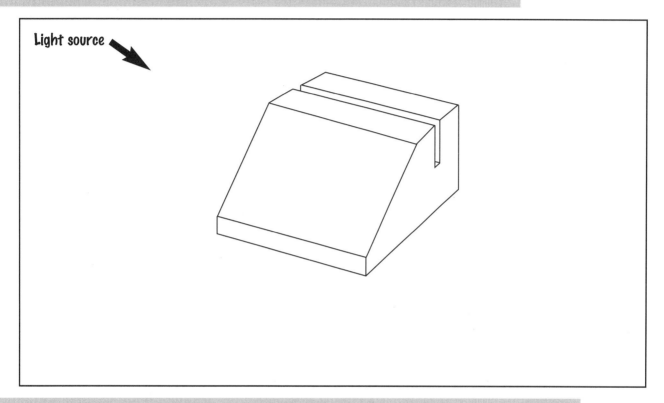

Light source

3. Add 'texture' to the following outline drawings so that they resemble the named materials.

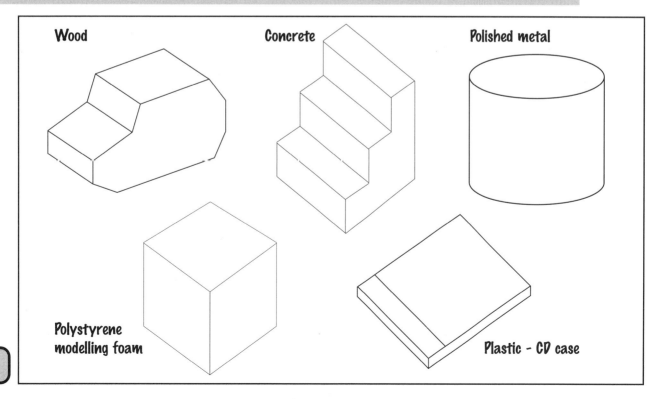

Wood

Concrete

Polished metal

Polystyrene
modelling foam

Plastic - CD case

1. Are the following statements true or false when using simple paints or coloured pencils? (Circle your answer)

(i) Red, yellow and blue are the only primary colours.	True / False
(ii) Primary colours are created by mixing any two colours.	True / False
(iii) Two primary colours give a secondary colour.	True / False
(iv) Green is made by mixing yellow and blue.	True / False
(v) Red is made by mixing purple and yellow.	True / False
(vi) Colours that work well together are complementary.	True / False

2. (a) What colour is used to darken the tone?

(a) ....

(b) What colour is used to lighten the tone?

(b) ....

3. Complete the hue diagrams using the colours indicated.

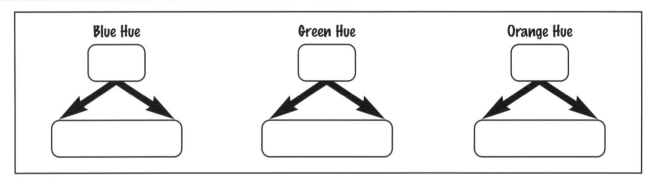

Blue Hue   Green Hue   Orange Hue

4. (a) When one colour blends into another colour it is called

C _ _ _ _ _   F _ _ _ _ _ _

(b) In the spaces blend (i) blue to purple, and (ii) red to yellow.

(i) Blue [   ] Purple

(ii) Red [   ] Yellow

5. Which colours are associated with the following products and situations?

(i) A leaflet about recycling garden waste. ....

(ii) A high energy sports drink. ....

(iii) An expensive box of chocolates. ....

(iv) The Islamic community. ....

(v) Good fortune by the Chinese community. ....

(vi) Warning of dangerous equipment or situation. ....

1. (a) What topics are well suited to planometric?

    ....

    (b) (i) What scale is used for verticals in 45° planometric? ....

    (ii) Why are verticals reduced?

    ....

    ....

    ....

2. An incomplete planometric line drawing of a model café interior is shown below. It shows the serving counter and two tables.

    (i) Complete the drawing by adding all details.

    (ii) Add a window to the longer wall.

    (iii) What is the angle of slope? ....

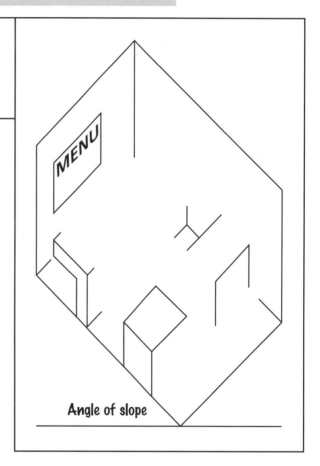

3. Scales are written as a ratio.
    Give the correct ratio for the following scales.

    (i) half full size   ....

    (ii) twice full size   ....

    (iii) full size   ....

    (iv) 10mm represents 10cm   ....

    (v) 10mm represents 100cm   ....

    (vi) 1cm represents $\frac{1}{2}$ metre   ....

Angle of slope

4. A sketch of a disposable camera is shown.

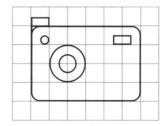

    (i) Make an enlarged drawing of the camera on the given grid.

    (ii) State the scale ratio used .... : ....

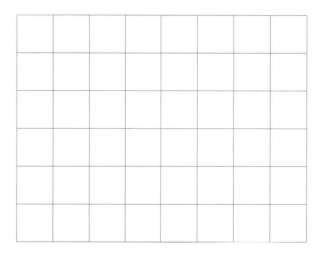

1. Complete the following isometric drawings.

(a) (i) a rectangular block, (L=30, W=20, H=10)

↓

(ii) The model steps shown

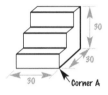

Corner A

(b) (i) a cube with sides 30mm long
  (ii) on each face construct a circle

↓

(c) A desk paper clip container is shown. Make an isometric sketch of the container. Corner A is given as a starting point.

A

↓

Corner A

(d) A professional quality eraser (rubber) is sold in a thin card sleeve. Complete the exploded sketch by adding the missing eraser.

Super ERASER

1.   Are the following statements true or false? (Circle your answer)

(i) The Eye Level is always on the horizon	True / False
(ii) The vanishing point(s) are where receding lines meet.	True / False
(iii) All vanishing points are on the horizon.	True / False
(iv) The further away an object is the smaller it looks.	True / False
(iv) Vertical lines meet on the horizon.	True / False
(vi) Horizontal lines always point at a vanishing point.	True / False

2.   (a) Complete the one point perspective sketch.

(b) Label the following points on the diagram below.

(i)   the vanishing point

(ii) the eye level

(iii) the horizon

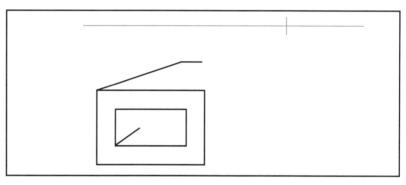

3.   Complete the one point perspective sketches of the menu card holder.
Note that the eye levels and vanishing points are different.

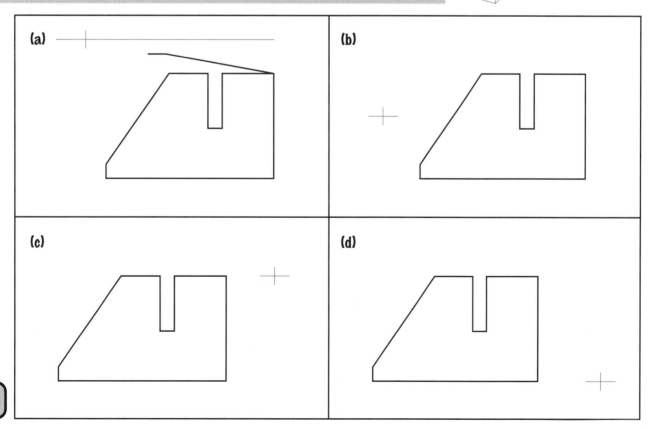

(a)

(b)

(c)

(d)

1. Below is an incomplete one point perspective sketch of a school corridor.

On the sketch, add the outlines of:
(i)   a notice board on the end wall
(ii) a classroom door on the left wall
(iii) windows along the right side
(iv) strip lights down the centre of the ceiling

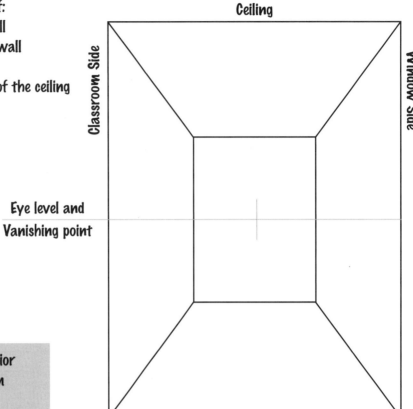

Ceiling

Classroom Side

Window Side

Eye level and
Vanishing point

Ground Level

2. In the space below draw an interior one point perspective of any room in your house or school.

Label the eye level and vanishing point. Draw any doors, windows or large items of furniture. Try to keep all items in proportion.

1. (a) Complete the two point perspective sketch of an audio cassette box.

Front Corner

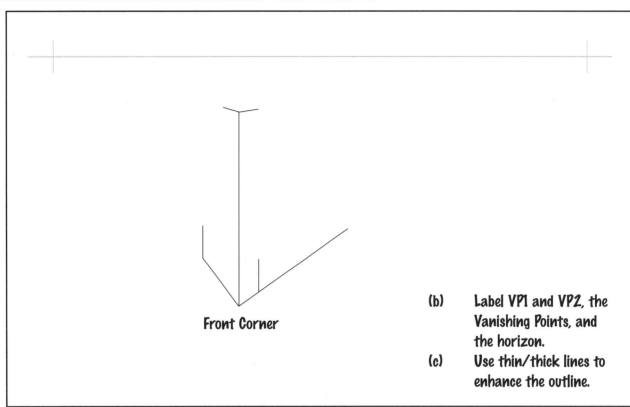

Front Corner

(b) Label VP1 and VP2, the Vanishing Points, and the horizon.

(c) Use thin/thick lines to enhance the outline.

2. A pencil desk tidy is shown. Draw a two-point perspective sketch of the desk tidy, do not include pencils or graphic.

PENCILS

1. A sketch of the point-of-sale packaging for an inkjet cartridge is given.

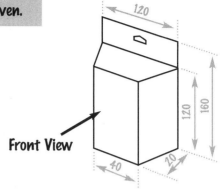

120

120 160

40 20

Front View

(a) Using British Standards draw, the front view, an end view and plan of the package half full size
(b) Add three major sizes
(c) Add the symbol for 3rd Angle Orthographic Projection
(d) Complete the name strip giving title, unit of measurement and scale used.
(Estimate any sizes not given)

Name strip

1.

1. Below is the outline plan of the ground floor of a wine bar/café, drawn to a scale of 1:100 (10mm =1m).
Using architectural symbols add the following features to the plan.
Do not include customer's tables and chairs.

(i)   a serving area with kitchen equipment
(ii) a store room
(iii) toilets, staff's and customer's, inc. WC, & basins
(iv) all walls
(v)   all doors inc. emergency exit
(vi) all windows
(vii) a spiral staircase to the first floor

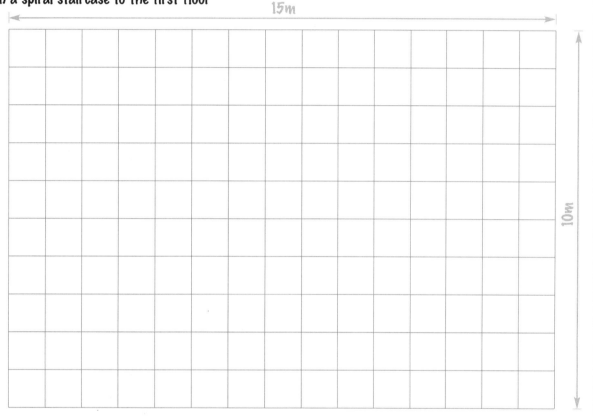

15m

10m

2. Using the same scale, sketch the wine bar/café frontage.

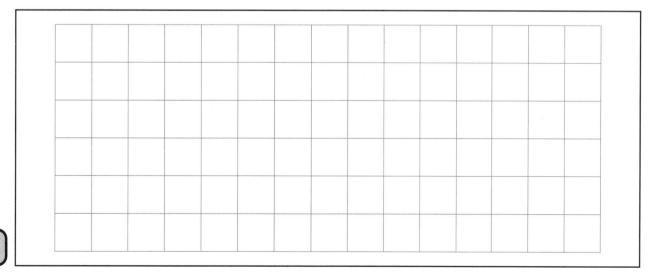

1.   The two developments (nets) below fold to make 3D containers.

(a) Show the way text must be printed for them to be correct when assembled.

(b) Draw freehand pictorial sketches of the assembled containers.

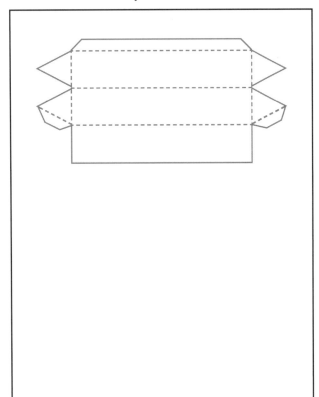

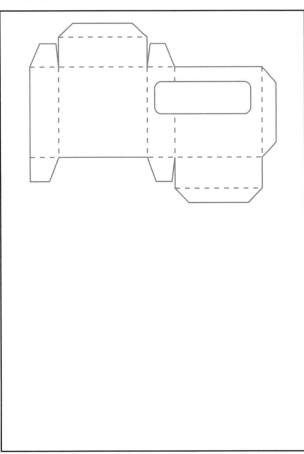

2.   Explain how when cutting several developments (nets) from one sheet of material waste can be reduced.

3.   What is

(a) a die cutter ?

(b) a creasing bar?

4.   (a) Briefly explain how a 'tuck in' lid is held secure.

(b) Give an advantage, for a retailer, of a 'crash lock' base.

1.   A good package has four functions, one is given, name the other three.

(i) To preserve   (ii) ....

(iii) ....   (iv) ....

2.   (a) What is the main difference between paper and board?

....

(b) Sketch what corrugated board looks like.

(c) On the sketch, label the 'flutes'.

(d) Why does corrugated board make a good outer box?

Corrugated Board

3.   Which paper-based material is used for a fruit juice container, and why?

....

4.   Complete the table which gives the common plastics and their uses in packaging.

PLASTIC	FULL NAME	USE 1	USE 2
PVC	Polyvinyl Chloride	Chilled food	
	Polyethylene Terephthalate		'Cook in the bag' food
			Ice cream packs
		Crisp packets	
		Bottle caps	Household chemicals
		Sandwich packs	

1.   **(a) What is 'ergonomics'?**

(b) Why should designers be concerned with ergonomics?

2.   **What are 'anthropometrics'?**

3.   **(a) Complete the chart by ranking in order of importance the factors to be considered in each of the given products.**
   (b) Add the focus of anthropometric research/data for each of the products. (The first one has been done for you)

Factors to consider in the design of the products	PRODUCTS				
	Car Air Freshener	Child's Activity Book	Fast food Containers	CD Player	Travel Game
Noise					
Shape					
Size					
Smell					
Temperature					
Weight					
Focus of Anthropometric Data	Adult's hand sizes				

1. (i) Sketch and colour the logos of two different products.
(ii) Give reasons for the suitability of the logos to their products.

Logo 1	Logo 2

(iii) Study one of the logos and explain what 'message' the colours communicate.

2. The following mark appears on some products, what does it stand for?

TM:

3. A brand name tells the customer about the product.

(a) Suggest a name for a new vegetarian restaurant.

(b) What qualities would you expect from a new drink called 'FIZZICLE' ?

4. (a) What is special about 'pictograms'?

(b) Give the meaning of each of the following pictograms often found on packages.

1. What is Typography?

---

2. Study the letter styles below and match each style to an application from the list given. Give a reason for the suitability of each.

Applications List: an expensive box of chocolates, a popular newspaper, a child's reading book, a theatre poster, a historical document, toiletry products

LETTER STYLE	TYPICAL APPLICATION	COMMENT
Study this letter style		
Study this letter style		
Study this letter style		
Study this letter style		
𝔖tudy this letter style		
Study this letter style		

---

3. The main text in this book uses a letter style called Marker. Why do you think this letter style was chosen? Give two reasons.

(i)

(ii)

---

4. (a) On the given letters, label the following parts: serif, stem, curve and continuous curve.

(b) Redraw the letters GP in the space below 'sanserif'

GP

1. When printing a commercial graphic product the method used depends on three basic factors, name them:

(i) _____   (ii) _____   (iii) _____

2. Name the five main printing methods.

(i) _____   (ii) _____   (iii) _____

(iv) _____   (v) _____

3. Complete the diagram showing the major different printing categories and their main processes.

PRINTING METHODS

SC _____ PRINTING   PL _____ PRINTING   IN _____

RE _____ PRINTING   DR _____ PRINTING

4. Which printing methods could be used in schools, by students working in Graphic Products, to produce a brick patterned paper for an architectural model.

_____
_____
_____

5. For each named printing method (i) sketch the basic process, and (ii) briefly explain it.

Letterpress

Notes:

Flexography

Notes:

Screen Printing

Notes:

Offset Lithography

Notes:

6. (a) Name the four processing colours used in printing.

(i) _____   (ii) _____   (iii) _____   (iv) _____

(b) What abbreviations are used to indicate the processing colours?

(c) Work can be printed from Computer Aided Design programs using the WYSIWYG principle. What does WYSIWYG stand for?

7. Selecting the most appropriate method for printing depends on several factors. Complete the chart below.

METHOD OF PRINTING	MAIN USES	MAIN ADVANTAGES	PRINT RUN	RELATIVE COST
Letterpress	eg. Good quality books, stationery.	Quality printed images	Short runs	Expensive
	eg. Packages, cartons, Point of Sale displays		Long runs	
	eg. High quality books, photographs, stamps.			Very expensive
		Good quality, uses rolls of paper.		
			From small numbers to several thousand	
Dry Printing		'WYSIWYG', good quality. Enlarging.		

1. Which type of ICT software package could be used for the following parts of a project? Name such a package/program that you have used or are aware of.

PROJECT COMPONENT	TYPE OF PACKAGE	NAME OF PACKAGE
A questionnaire		
Drawing graphs		
Decorations on box		
Advertising Flyer		

2. (a) What does DTP stand for?

(b) What is special about DTP packages?

3. Graphic packages fall into three main kinds depending on their use. Complete the diagram, giving one advantage and one disadvantage for each.

KINDS OF GRAPHIC PACKAGES

Advantage:	Advantage:	Advantage:
Disadvantage:	Disadvantage:	Disadvantage:

4. (a) What is a 'pixel'?

(b) What does 'CAD' stand for?

(c) What is 'clip art'?

1. (a) What does 'www.' stand for?

   (b) What is 'email'?

2. Computer systems consist of input, processing and output devices. Shown below is a selection of equipment. Name each and state whether it is an input or output device. (One has been done for you)

Keyboard Input			

3. Electronic data, such as coursework, can be stored on several devices. Identify the following storage devices.

4. (a) What does CAM stand for?

   (b) Give three advantages and two disadvantages of using CAM over traditional methods of industrial production.

Advantage 1	
Advantage 2	
Advantage 3	

Disadvantage 1	
Disadvantage 2	

1. The following Design Process is for a coursework project - a model mobile phone.
Complete the chart showing how ICT can be used to improve both the quality and accuracy of the work.
'The Problem' stage has been done for you.

DESIGN PROCESS STAGE	ICT APPLICATION OR EQUIPMENT	WHAT THE APPLICATION IS USED TO PRODUCE
THE PROBLEM	(i) The Internet	(i) Use search engine to find websites of manufacturers & shops to identify new trends
RESEARCH	(i) (ii) Spreadsheets (iii) Digital Camera (iv)	(i) Questionnaires (ii) (iii) (iv) Contacting Industry
SPECIFICATIONS	(i)	(i) List of design requirements
DESIGN IDEAS	(i) (ii) (iii)	(i) Draw ideas. (ii) Try different colour schemes (iii) Input images of similar products & modify them
DEVELOPMENT	(i) (ii) (iii)	(i) (ii) (iii)
FINAL DESIGN	(i) (ii) (iii)	(i) Working drawings, nets of package (ii) Presentation drawings (iii) Instructional sheets
PLANNING (order of making)	(i) Word processing (ii) Spreadsheets	(i) (ii)
MAKING	(i) (ii) Colour Printer	(i) (i) (ii) Flyers, instructions, package surface developments/nets
EVALUATION & MODIFICATIONS	(i) (ii) (iii)	(i) (ii) (iii)

1. CAD/CAM has replaced many traditional graphics skills,
eg. designing and making of signs for buildings and shops, on vans and in public spaces.

(a) Give two advantages to the manufacturer of CAD/CAM when designing a new sign for a cafe.

Advantage 1:

Advantage 2:

(b) How can a digital image of a building's front on a computer screen assist in the designing of a cafe's exterior sign?

2. Briefly explain how CAD/CAM is used to reduce costs.

3. Name three savings to the manufacturer of using CAM to print and cut graphic products on self-adhesive vinyl sheet.

1st saving:

2nd saving:

3rd saving:

4. What is the advantage of storing a client's final design on a computer system?

1. Complete the table below: name the four types of movement, briefly explain each and give an example of that type of motion.

TYPE OF MOVEMENT	EXPLANATION	EXAMPLE
(i)		
(ii)		
(iii)		
(iv)		

2. How many basic types, or classes, of lever are there?

3. For each of the following levers label the fulcrum, load and effort.

  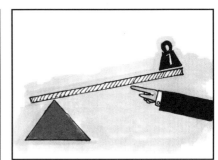

4. (a) Three applications of levers are shown.

Complete the diagrams by adding and labelling the fulcrum, load and effort

(b)(i) Which of the above are examples of a lever acting as a force multiplier?

(ii) Which of the above is an example of a lever acting as a movement multiplier?

1. Complete the sentence by filling in the missing words.

> Cranks and _____ are simple devices which convert _____ motion
>
> to _____ motion (or vice _____).

2. Look at the power hacksaw in your school's Resistant Materials workshop. Make a sketch of it showing how the crank and slider work. Add brief notes to help explain your sketch.

3. Complete the sentence by filling in the missing words.

> A rotary cam is a device which converts _____ into _____

4. A 2D diagram of a simple nodding toy with cam and follower is shown.

(a) Label (i) the circular cam
     (ii) a lever
     (iii) the follower
     (iv) a pivot
     (v) a crankshaft
(b) Use arrows to indicate
     direction of any motion

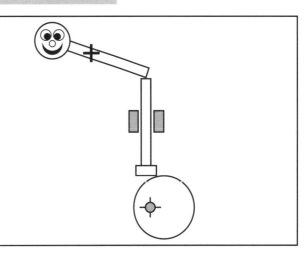

5. Name these three common types of cam.

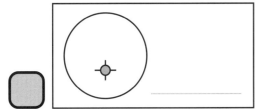
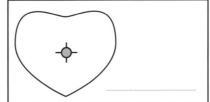
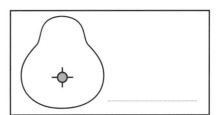

1. Complete the statements below and sketch each type of spring, showing the direction of the forces acting on the spring.

A spring that resists a 'pulling' force is an _____ spring	A spring that resists a 'pushing' force is a _____ spring

2. What is special about the levers used in this child's party toy?

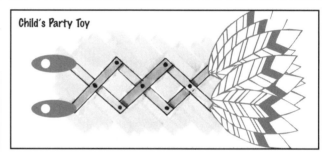

Child's Party Toy

_____

_____

3. Below are the outlines of the front of two card toys.
In (i) when the tab is pulled the face 'pops' out from behind the wall.
In (ii) when the tab is pulled its hat moves down and the ears 'waggle'.
In both cases, complete the mechanism seen from the back of the card, showing how they work. Label the important features eg. supports, pivots, glued areas

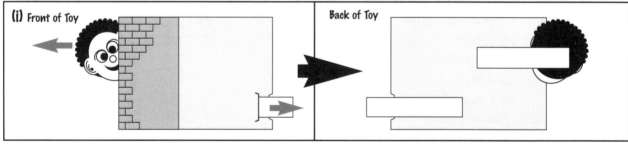

(i) Front of Toy   Back of Toy

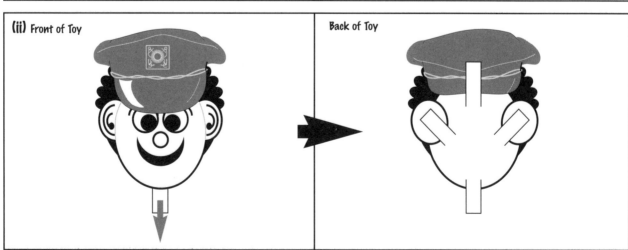

(ii) Front of Toy   Back of Toy

1. Complete the following by adding the missing words from the list given. (You will not use them all).

Gears are like _____ , transferring one _____ to another. Gear wheels may be linked by _____ or _____ . Gears are used as force _____ or _____ to make things go _____ or _____ .

linkages	slower	cog	faster	motion	belts
multipliers	chains	ratio	reducers	teeth	internal

2. (a) Label the parts of the gears indicated on the diagrams below.

(b) Show the direction of motion using arrows.

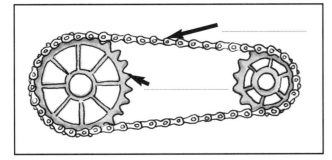
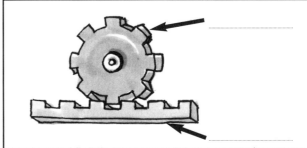

3. (a) How many times does A turn compared to B in the diagram below?

(b) If A turns 20 times in a minute, how many times will B turn in a minute?

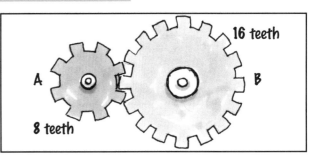

16 teeth

A   B

8 teeth

4. In the space below draw and label sketches showing how a pulley and belt can be made using only modelling material.

1.   **(a) (i) What is scoring?**

(ii) Why is it done?

(b) What equipment is used in scoring?

2.   **(a) Study the sketch of a 'pop-up' greeting card and in the space show how you can make it using thin card.**

(b) It was found that in the completed card the folding design sloped forwards. With sketches and notes explain how the design can be made to be vertical when opened.

3. Study the sketch of a clown's bow tie and with sketches and notes show how it is made from thin card.

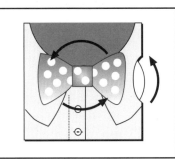

4. (a) Name this component which is often used in rotary mechanisms.

This component is a ....

(b) This toy has a rotary mechanism using the component named above. As the wheel is turned four different faces appear at the window. Draw an exploded sketch of the card toy.

window

1. Study the given sketch and draw its surface development (net), labelling all fold and score lines.

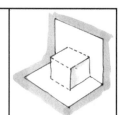

2. From the given surface development (net), sketch in 3-D, the card mechanism it produces.

(NET)

3. Look carefully at the example of an incised mechanism and use sketches and brief notes to show how it can be made. (Hint, a little extra card is required).

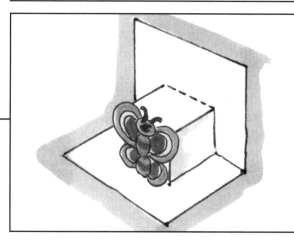

4. Study the example of a sliding mechanism card and explain with sketches and notes how it is made.

Screen

HELLO!

The face slides out from behind the screen.

5. The card above needs a pull to move the face out and a push to return it behind the wall. Use sketches and notes to show how you could use an elastic band to make the mechanism return automatically.

6. Study the given diagram of a layer mechanism.

(a) Name a GRAPHIC PRODUCT, other than a greetings card, which makes use of this mechanism.

Strips of card forming squares and rectangles

(b) The size and position of the card strips is important.

(i) With notes and sketches explain why the strips of card must form squares or rectangles.

(ii) How far can the card strip stand out from the base before it is seen when the assembly is closed flat?

(i)

(ii)

7. The vertical surfaces of the card strips can be used to support other images or shapes. In the space below design a layer mechanism for a greeting card which displays the word 'Hello' when opened.

1. Briefly explain what is meant by product analysis.

....
....
....
....

2. Give 3 uses for a scaled architectural model of a pagoda.

Architectural Model of a Pagoda

3. Briefly explain why the unit cost of a product is less when it is made in larger numbers.

....
....
....
....

4. (a) What is meant by the term 'Target Market'?

....

(b) Give two marketing techniques which are used to identify target groups.

(i) ....

(ii) ....

(c) Market research produces information which can be displayed graphically.
Give four methods of displaying information pictorially.

(i) ....   (ii) ....

(iii) ....   (iv) ....

1. It is often useful to record how a product has changed over the years.

(a) A 'time line' is a graphical method used to illustrate a product's evolution.
What is meant by the term 'time line'?

> ....
> ....

(b) Study the images of photographic cameras below and rearrange them in order of development.

A	B	C	D	E
35 mm SLR	Disposable	'Box' type	Digital	Tripod

1st (Oldest)	2nd	3rd	4th	5th (Newest)
....	....	....	....	....

2. Compare these two products: a disposable camera and a 35mm SLR camera.

CRITERIA	DISPOSABLE CAMERA	35mm SINGLE LENS REFLEX
Ease of use		
Changing the film		
Environmental issues		
Packaging issues		
Useful life of camera		

3. (a) What is 'ergonomics'?

> ....
> ....

(b) What is meant by 'Anthropometrical Data'?

> ....
> ....

1. If a product is to be cleaned, what properties are necessary in the materials used to make it?

(i) .... (ii) ....

(iii) .... (iv) ....

2. (a) Name the material and manufacturing process used to make the following products.

A MOBILE PHONE CASING	MINERAL WATER BOTTLE
Material	Material ....
Manufacturing Process	Manufacturing Process ....

(b) Name the appropriate industrial printing process for these products.

CAFE MENU CARD	SUPERMARKET PLASTIC CARRIER BAG
....	....

3. In the space name, sketch and label one of the manufacturing processes named in Question 2.

This process is ....

4. A sketch of a carbonated drink can is shown below, annotate it with reference to the materials and processes used.

COLA

1. Product labelling and the materials used play an important role in environmental issues.

(a) Briefly explain these symbols which appear on many graphic products.

♻	....	🗑	....

(b) What is the difference between re-using and re-filling? Give examples.

....

....

....

....

(c) Why is it necessary to use new and not recycled materials in food packaging?

....

....

....

(d) Name the basic raw material used in the products below, and state if they are renewable or non-renewable resources:

PRODUCT	RAW MATERIAL	RENEWABLE/NON-RENEWABLE
Newspapers	....	....
Carrier bags	....	....

2. The following symbols are on many graphic products. Give the full meaning of each and an example of the type of product where it can be expected

$C\epsilon$	.... Example:
e	.... Example:

3. A new fast food restaurant is opening in your town.

(i) Complete the ideas web of different ways of promoting the restaurant so that your target group is aware of its opening.

(ii) Sketch a pictogram to represent each promotion method. (An example is given)

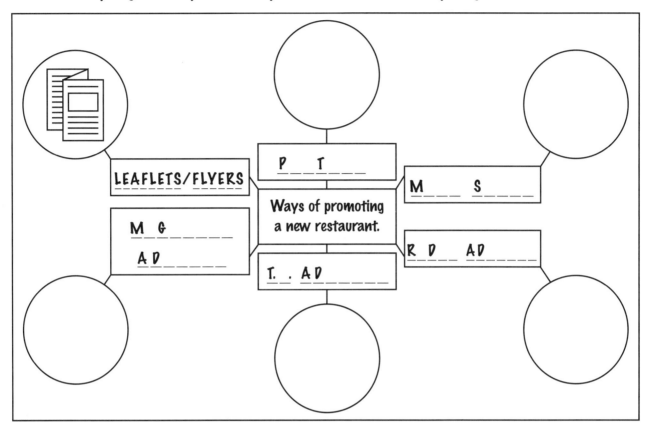

LEAFLETS/FLYERS

P _ T _ _ _ _ _ _

Ways of promoting a new restaurant.

M _ _ _ S _ _ _ _ _

M _ G _ _ _ _ _ _ A D _ _ _ _ _ _

T _ . _ A D _ _ _ _ _ _

R D _ A D _ _ _ _

4. Successful graphic products are also 'aesthetically pleasing'.
Briefly explain what is meant by the term 'aesthetically pleasing'.

5. If the quantity of a product produced greatly increases how would it affect the following factors?

(i) Method of production

(ii) Total cost and unit cost

PLASTICS

1. Briefly give three points which must be considered when selecting a material for a product.

Point 1: ....

Point 2: ....

Point 3: ....

2. Plastics are important materials.

(a) What is the raw material from which plastics are made? ....

(b) Is this a renewable or non-renewable source? ....

3. (a) Name two different types or groups of plastic.

Type 1 ....   Type 2 ....

(b) Explain, with notes and diagrams, the differences between the two types of plastic with reference to
   (i) the structure   (ii) effect of heat   (iii) the environment

1. Complete the table of plastics commonly used in graphic products.

Name of Plastic and Abbreviation	Thermosetting Plastic or Thermoplastic	Typical use in a Graphic Product model	A Sketch illustrating its use.
Low Density Polythene ( )	Thermoplastic	1. Plastic Carrier Bag 2.	
e.g Perspex		1. 2. Represent glass in models	
(ER)		1. 2.	
		1. Modelling a camera body 2.	
(PVC)		1. 2.	
	Thermosetting Plastic	1. Encapsulation 2.	

1. A car air freshener is shown in a 'blister pack'. The plastic character contains the perfume.

(a) Name the production method used to form the plastic air character.

(b) Use sketches and notes to explain how the freshener is made. DO NOT include the packaging.

2. (a) Name three plastics which are suitable for extruding into rods and tubes.

(i) _____

(ii) _____

(iii) _____

(b) A student wishes to make and package a ball point pen. The main part of the pen is made from extruded clear plastic tube. Using sketches and notes explain the industrial method of making the tube.

1. **(a) Name two products which use a container made by the 'blow moulding' process.**

(i) _____ (ii) _____

(b) In the spaces below show the key stages involved in making a product by the 'blow moulding' method. Label the diagrams.

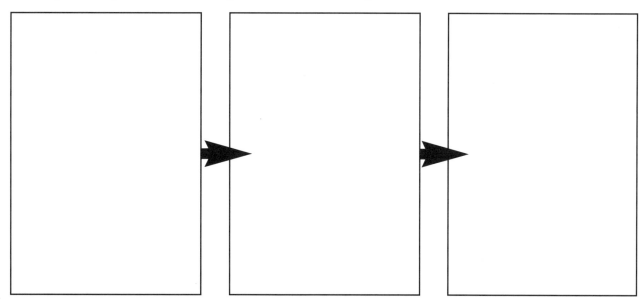

2. A student is designing a perfume bottle together with its promotional material. A distinctive screw top is required.

(a) Name an industrial method of making a perfume bottle top.

_____

(b) Using sketches and notes explain the industrial method of making the perfume bottle top.

1. Give three advantages of rotational moulding over other industrial methods of shaping plastics.

(i)

(ii)

(iii)

2. (a) Name two products made by rotational moulding.

(i)   (ii)

(b) Give the full name of the plastic used in this process and explain why it is suitable.

3. (a) (i) Name the method of forming plastic shown here.

(ii) Name the type of plastic used in this method,
(iii) Give an example of the type of plastic.

(ii)   (iii)

(b) What is a jig?

(c) Explain with sketches and notes how 10 identical plastic corners
are formed to have a right angle (90°) at the given position.

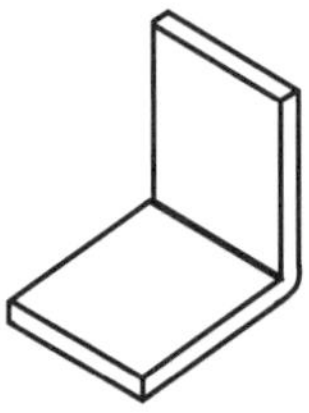

1. A student wishes to model a design for a mobile phone. A mould made from MDF has been shaped.

(a) Explain, with sketches and notes, a method for forming plastic sheet to the shape of the mould.

(b) Why is polystyrene a suitable material for this process?

(c) The shaping of the mould is important. Why should the sides of the mould be tapered?

2. (a) What is calendering?

(b) What products are made by this method and what plastics are used?.

3. Of all the processes considered, why is compression moulding the odd one out?

4. Which process could be modelled with a hot glue gun and a small cavity mould?

1. A student is designing a range of food containers and is making a card chip package, as shown.

(i) Rearrange the following stages into an order of making
(ii) List equipment required
(iii) Estimate the time you would expect to spend on each stage
(iv) Add any other factors that would help you realise your design
    The first stage has been done for you.

STAGES (In random order):
- Cut out the shape
- Draw the net (surface development)
- Draw the design on the net (surface development)
- Assemble
- Fold and crease
- Render the design

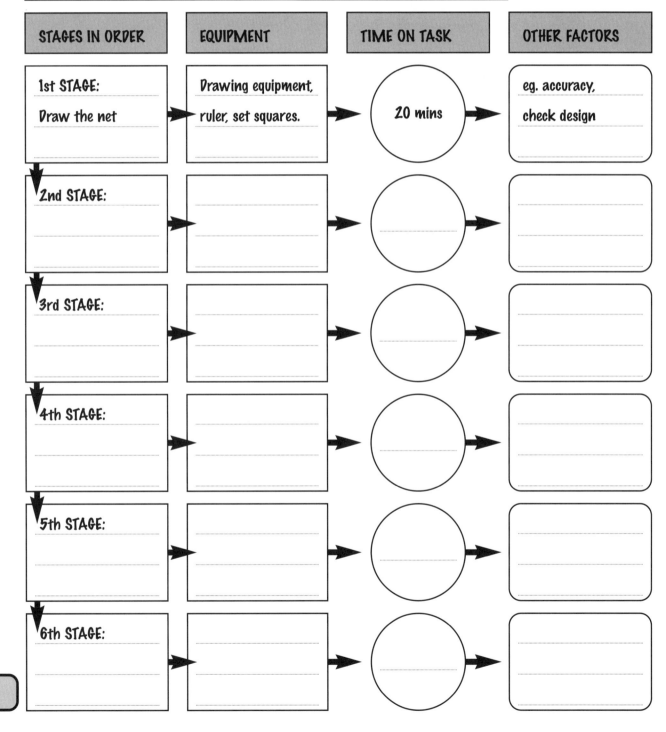

STAGES IN ORDER	EQUIPMENT	TIME ON TASK	OTHER FACTORS
1st STAGE: Draw the net	Drawing equipment, ruler, set squares.	20 mins	eg. accuracy, check design
2nd STAGE:			
3rd STAGE:			
4th STAGE:			
5th STAGE:			
6th STAGE:			

1. What is a 'flow chart'?

2. Name these flow chart symbols and give a brief description of their meaning.

3. Complete the flow chart for vacuum forming a plastic box, by adding the correct symbols and arrows.

4. A cafe requires 10 perspex table number signs. Draw a flow diagram showing how they are made using line bending and a jig.

60° 7

START

↓

SWITCH HEATER ON

APPLY HEAT

IS THE PLASTIC HOT ENOUGH?

RAISE MOULD

SWITCH VACUUM ON

IS MOULDING CORRECT?

REMOVE HEAT

SWITCH VACUUM OFF

REMOVE MOULDING

STOP

1. Explain the following methods of production:

(a) 'One-off' Production

(b) Batch Production

(c) Mass Production

(d) Continuous Production

2. Give one advantage and one disadvantage of 'Just In Time' production.

Advantage:

Disadvantage:

3. A range of projects with a high graphics content is shown below. Tick a box to indicate which method of production is most appropriate for that project. (One has been done for you).

	Cafe frontage	Headed note paper	Teenage Magazine	Postage stamps	Point of sale display	Easter egg box	Play area model	Pop concert t-shirt	Board game	Fashion show	'Cola' type drink cans
'One-off' Production	✓										
Batch Production											
Mass Production											
Continuous Production											

1. Briefly explain what is meant by 'quality control'.

2. (a) Manufactured products are often made to a stated 'tolerance'.
What is meant by, 'ten pieces of Perspex have to be cut to a length of 150mm +/- 2mm'?

(b) Use annotated sketches to explain a device you could make
which would quickly check if the Perspex is within tolerance.

3. It can be very expensive for industry to achieve 'ZERO FAULTS'. Explain the
meaning of the 'e' mark on packet goods such as sweets and soap powder.

e 250g

4. (a) Commercially printed material has other quality control checks. Briefly explain what colour bars are.

(b) These three marks have a similar meaning. What are they and what is their importance.

(c) Briefly explain what is meant by 'visual checks'.

5. Briefly explain the difference between 'quality control' and 'quality assurance'.

6. A commercially produced 'pop-up' book is to be tested. Explain why destructive testing may be required rather than non-destructive testing.

1. What is an evaluation?

2. Once faced with your final outcome, write FIVE questions you could ask yourself about the product, which could form the basis for an evaluation report.

(i)

(ii)

(iii)

(iv)

(v)

3. Another way of evaluating your product would be to carry out a 'specification check', which could be in the form of a table. In the space below sketch part of a 'spec/check' table.

4. A good evaluation often shows up faults or imperfections in a design. What should you do when they are identified?

1. Using one of your coursework projects complete the evaluation guidelines below. Remember not all the headings may apply to your chosen project. Try to give reasons and not just simple 'Yes' or 'No' answers.

TITLE OF PROJECT:

WEIGHT/SIZE - Did the size or weight affect how it worked?

ERGONOMICS - Is it comfortable to hold and use?

Explain whether it is environmentally friendly or not.

SAFETY - Is it safe for the intended users to use?

COST - What is the estimated cost of your model?

What are the 'hidden costs' of manufacturing it?

QUANTITY - What scale of production will be used commercially?

Would any features have to be re-designed if large numbers were made?

MARKET SECTOR - How does it compare to rival products?

Does it attract the intended target group?